Poems of Robert Herrick

The Crowell Poets

Under the editorship of Lillian Morrison

POEMS OF WILLIAM BLAKE
Selected by Amelia H. Munson

POEMS OF ROBERT BROWNING
Selected by Rosemary Sprague

POEMS OF STEPHEN CRANE
Selected by Gerald D. McDonald

POEMS OF EMILY DICKINSON
Selected by Helen Plotz

POEMS OF RALPH WALDO EMERSON
Selected by J. Donald Adams

POEMS OF WILLIAM S. GILBERT
Selected by William Cole

POEMS OF ROBERT HERRICK
Selected by Winfield Townley Scott

POEMS OF JOHN KEATS
Selected by Stanley Kunitz

POEMS OF HENRY WADSWORTH LONGFELLOW
Selected by Edmund Fuller

POEMS OF EDGAR ALLAN POE
Selected by Dwight Macdonald

POEMS OF WILLIAM SHAKESPEARE
Selected by Lloyd Frankenberg

POEMS OF ALFRED, LORD TENNYSON
Selected by Ruth Greiner Rausen

POEMS OF WALT WHITMAN
Selected by Lawrence Clark Powell

POEMS OF WILLIAM WORDSWORTH
Selected by Elinor Parker

POEMS OF
ROBERT HERRICK

Selected by Winfield Townley Scott

DRAWINGS BY ELLEN RASKIN

Thomas Y. Crowell Company   New York

CONTENTS

PREFATORY NOTE

No SELECTION from Robert Herrick's more than 1,400 poems can be assembled with the conviction that here are all the finest. Many of his lyrics are famously inevitable; after those the editor is necessarily on his own taste. At the least, I feel certain this book represents Herrick in all his moods as a poet and his skills as a craftsman and that it contains much of his most beautiful verse; if it should send a reader on to the complete works, that would be its most rewarding purpose.

Myself, I have used two editions: *The Poems of Robert Herrick*, edited by L. C. Martin (Oxford University Press), a stately volume; and *The Complete Poetry of Robert Herrick*, edited by J. Max Patrick (Doubleday and Company Anchor Book), heavily and usefully annotated.

The text here has been modernized as faithfully to Herrick's text as I could make it. In a tiny number of instances I have taken the liberty of substituting a modern word where Herrick's is so obsolete as to be undiscoverable in a large dictionary. It is an outrageous liberty to take, but I have wished to avoid in this edition—insofar as possible—the scholarly look of footnotes.

Scholars have never discerned any formal arrangement of Herrick's poems, save the obviously introductory and valedictory pieces, and this selection mostly orders the poems as they occur in *Hesperides* and *His Noble Numbers*.

I have consulted various biographical sources, but my greatest debt is to Marchette Chute's characteristically excellent *Two Gentle Men* (E. P. Dutton and Company), a dual biography of Herrick and George Herbert. In these matters of research, I wish to acknowledge the essential helpfulness of David A. Jonah, Librarian of Brown University, and F. Warren Roberts, Director of the Humanities Research Center of the University of Texas.

This book is for my son Douglas Herrick Scott, great-grandson of Robert Herrick (1866–1942), of Boston, Massachusetts.

W. T. S.

MEADOW-VERSE

Oft as your field shall her old age renew
Herrick shall make the meadow-verse for you.

—*Robert Herrick*

Robert Herrick was born in 1591 in Goldsmith's Row, Cheapside, London, a district closely associated with William Shakespeare. In 1607, when young Herrick entered upon his apprenticeship as a goldsmith, he lived at his uncle's house in Wood Street, through which you can still walk to Silver Street, where Shakespeare once had lodgings. In those latter years Shakespeare's theater was across the river—over on the other side of the Thames—and Herrick's poetry shows no awareness of Shakespeare; Herrick's contemporary master and idol was Ben Jonson. Nevertheless, Herrick was a full-grown nineteen when the great playwright departed for Stratford (often to return to the city as a visitor), and London was not so large that the aspiring young poet might never have passed the slight, small-bearded older man. One hopes these two did pass, however anonymously, and with an exchange of glances, for no poet in the language except Shakespeare wrote lovelier, purer lyrics than Robert Herrick's, and perhaps even Shakespeare did not achieve so many.

The exact date of Herrick's birth, as of his death, is unknown. It is recorded that he was baptized on August 24, 1591. He was the seventh child (and fourth son) of Nicholas and Julian Stone Herrick. His mother's odd name teases one, for of all the names of Herrick's poetic mistresses—and they seem to have been just that: poetic—the overwhelming favorite is "Julia." Whether or not there was a real woman whom the name represented, certainly Herrick loved the name.

The Herricks were a distinguished family in Leicestershire, an affectionate, close-knit, happy clan, landowners and prosperous ironmongers. But Nicholas, son of John, took off for London to become apprenticed in the craft of goldsmithing. Almost thirty years later he married Julian Stone, in 1582. Ten years after, in poor health, Nicholas made his will, and he either fell or deliberately plunged to his death from a window high in his house in Goldsmith's Row Robert Herrick was then a baby not much over a year old, and Julian was left with him and (the eldest child having died) five other children, also, she was pregnant.

Proved suicide in that era meant that the government could confiscate the property of the deceased, which in Nicholas' case was considerable. And suspicion of suicide was very strong. But Julian, in her own right financially well endowed, had some eminent and influential connections, the overseers of her husband's will, his brothers Robert and Sir William Herrick; and in the end she retained her inheritance.

Sir William became a key figure in the formative years of his nephew Robert. When Robert was sixteen—and this is the first fact we know about him after his baptism—his Uncle William took the boy into his house as an apprentice goldsmith. The term would be for ten years. Robert bore with the increasingly uncongenial labor for six years. Already he had meadow-verse on his mind.

So in 1613 he went off to St. John's College in Cambridge. He entered as a fellow commoner, which not only signifies that he enjoyed special privileges but also that he had to pay double fees. This he did not enjoy, and his known history at St. John's consists of letters to Sir William dunning his uncle for money—apparently money of Robert's own, but inadequate for the debts he accumulated. Cheaper living had something to do with his transferring to Trinity Hall. There he studied law, which must have been as antipathetic to his true intent as goldsmithing had been. In any case, he took a B.A. in 1617 and an M.A. in 1620.

Among the friends Herrick made at the college were Clipseby Crew—to be celebrated several times in the *Hesperides* poems—and John Weekes. Following a few more years of unrecorded activity, which for the poet very likely included intimacy with the Ben Jonson circle in London, Herrick and Weekes appeared together before the Bishop of Peterborough on April 24, 1623. The bishop ordained them as deacons in the Church of England and on the very next day—without the customary interval—as priests in the Church.

Did these two young men serve as noblemen's chaplains? No clues have ever come to light. When we next hear of them, the news is rather astonishing.

King Charles's favorite, the great, glamorous, powerful and pig-headed Duke of Buckingham, unluckily decided to mount a war against France. On the first of July 1627, he commanded a fleet that sailed for the Isle of Ré. Two of his chaplains aboard were John Weekes and Robert Herrick. Of all the gentle poets who have ever gone to war, surely here were the gentlest. The friends survived months of military blunders and fiascos. Of Buckingham's 6,000 men only 2,000 lived to return to England, and one dissident among them, John Felton, the next year stabbed the duke to death.

A result—if such it was—of the campaign was a far more fortunate one for Robert Herrick and English poetry. The King gave Herrick the vicarage of Dean Prior in Devon. He was installed as vicar in late October of 1630, and there—except for the thirteen-year interruption of the Rebellion—he lived a rural village life as a bachelor clergyman, tending his parish, preaching and writing, his remaining forty-four years.

Decades after Herrick's death an ancient lady, Dorothy King, recalled that he had a pet pig which he taught to drink out of a tankard, and also—although Anthony Wood declared that Herrick's sermons were "florid and witty"—that on one occasion he cursed his congregation in exasperation for their inattention and hurled the text of his sermon at them.

He did not find the peasantry inspiring, and amidst Devon's rich farming country there were moors as forbidding as Emily Brontë's. More than once in his verse he expressed the dissatisfactions of an exiled Londoner. Yet Herrick (who pretty surely had memories of his own family's lands in Leicestershire) was essentially a rural poet, and his life in Devon had its mitigations: his faithful housekeeper, Prudence Baldwin (whom he made immortal), and the mutual affection between himself and the gentry, notably Sir Edward Giles and his relatives, the Yard family. One senses that here was an easygoing vicar, often lonely, but delighting in the countryside's customs, traditions, celebrations. He had, however frugally, "a living," which in his mind was not so much to support a man of the cloth as to support a dedicated poet.

He traveled to London, probably in 1640, to negotiate for the publication of his book of poems—announcement of the collection was registered—but the project fell through. Obviously he tarried, for he was "reported for nonresidence" in Devon.

Herrick was soon to spend a much longer time in London. In 1642 civil war erupted: Puritans against Royalists, Puritans and Presbyterians against the State Church, Parliament against the King. Devon's cathedral town, Exeter, was captured the next year by the Royalists, who lost it in 1646. (Devon was predominantly anti-Royalist.) As a vicar of the King's Church and, of course, a Royalist, Herrick was ejected from Dean Prior, and he went to London. Here are his sentiments:

His Return to London

FROM THE dull confines of the drooping west,
To see the day spring from the pregnant east,
Ravished in spirit, I come; nay more, I fly
To thee, blest place of my nativity!
Thus, thus, with hallowed foot I touch the ground,
With thousand blessings by thy fortune crowned.
O fruitful genius that bestowest here
An everlasting plenty, year by year.

O place! O people! manners! framed to please
All nations, customs, kindreds, languages!
I am a free-born Roman; suffer then
That I amongst you live a citizen.
London my home is: though by hard fate sent
Into a long and irksome banishment;
Yet since called back, henceforward let me be,
O native country, repossessed by thee!
For, rather than I'll to the west return,
I'll beg of thee first here to have my urn.
Weak I am grown and must in short time fall;
Give thou my sacred relics burial.

From 1647 until 1660 relatives presumably took care of him.
We know only one fact about him during all that time, but it is
the fact of supreme importance: in 1648 his book was published,
*Hesperides: or, the Works both Humane & Divine of Robert Herrick,
Esq.* "Hesperides" in Greek and Roman mythology was that
garden—or the nymphs who protected it—which contained the
sacred golden apples. These *Works*, which include *His Noble
Numbers: His Pious Pieces*, were "Printed for John Williams,
and Francis Eglesfield, and are to be sold at the Crown and
Marygold in Saint Paul's Churchyard." Twenty years later
there were still copies for sale, but scholars think not that
Hesperides sold poorly, but that the printing may have been a
large one, since Herrick was a widely known poet and in
manuscript circulation (the custom of the era) only John Donne
surpassed him.

Robert Herrick was fifty-seven years old. After this did he cease to write? The answer seems to be: On the whole, yes. Outside his book, there are a dozen or two poems attributed to him, some with reliability, but none which ranks with his finest. We have to remember how short the average life span was in that England; a Shakespeare could die at only 52 and not be considered to have perished untimely—"only" is our word and not the seventeenth century's. So Herrick at fifty-seven no doubt regarded himself as an old man; and indeed he several times wrote as such, years before his book was gathered and issued. Nevertheless, he lived on to the age of eighty-three.

But the rest of the dates run quickly. In 1649 King Charles was beheaded and Oliver Cromwell's Commonwealth established. In 1660 King Charles II returned to England and Robert Herrick to his vicarage—and to his good "Prew"—in Dean Prior. In 1674 Herrick died (the same year as a poet seventeen years his junior, John Milton). He was buried in an unmarked grave at Dean Prior on October 15. In mid-nineteenth century, when Herrick's almost lost reputation had been firmly re-established, a collateral descendant erected in the parish church a monument to the poet; but no one knows just where Herrick's bones lie.

Herrick's poetry had practically a death and a resurrection. During the seventeenth century, poems of his were frequently reprinted; yet his name all but vanished when that century ended. The eighteenth century scarcely knew of his existence: readers sometimes remembered his epigrams, tidily to the taste of a couplet-bound poetic era dominated by such a practitioner as Alexander Pope and such a literary lawgiver as Samuel

Johnson. For the most part these epigrams now seem slight, and often obvious, banal, vulgar, even sadistic, and in bad taste. They are the least of his work—incomparably beneath the lyrics that sing at heaven's gate.

By the early 1800s those lyrics began to be rediscovered: the Romantic Age was there to appreciate them. A selection of his poems published in 1810 was the first Herrick book since the original *Hesperides* of 1648. Then, in 1823, there was "a very elegant reprint" of his entire work. The phrase is Richard Ryan's. In Volume II of his three-volume *Poetry and Poets* (London, 1826), a mélange of criticism and chitchat, Ryan characterized Herrick as "the sweetest of songsters in an age which produced Waller, Carew, Suckling, and Lovelace." Remarking that Herrick is "little known," Ryan regrets that the poet has not been anthologized. He complains that some of Herrick's compositions "are a disgrace to the volume in which they are found," an allusion of course to the vicar's occasional bawdry and one which Ryan was not alone in making. All the same, Ryan concludes on a note of highest admiration for the lyric beauty of Herrick's poems.

The tradition behind Herrick's verse—and this explains his naughtiness as well as his marvelous delicacy—is Latin. We know nothing of Herrick's schooling save the little about his college years, yet it is certain he knew the poems of Horace, Virgil, Martial, Catullus, Tibullus, Ovid, Propertius. He was a Roman seventeenth-century English poet. And in his own time the tradition was focused in that fine classicist, Ben Jonson. Herrick sometimes imitated Jonson's verse and he always worshiped Jonson. As a young man in London, Herrick sat at Jonson's feet and he considered himself among the "sons of Ben." Yet there is a question as to whether he was accepted in the inner circle. When an anthology was made in memory of Jonson, no Herrick poem was included. Unhappily, one detects a touch of pathos here. Did the disciples—how blindly!—not accept Herrick as quite belonging? No matter now: Herrick is supreme among them.

Although Marchette Chute quite rightly calls *Hesperides* one of the loveliest books in the language, it is not wounded by selection. I have mentioned the epigrams, and a few samples of what seem to me the wiser ones are included here. There are other, dimmer, passages in *Hesperides*. For instance, Herrick's tributes to royalty and noblemen tend to be of a more political than poetical interest. Also Herrick indulges in whimsy— usually amorous—which rises no higher than valentine sentiments; this is his too slight mode, his *vers de societé*. And, like any prolific poet, Herrick is repetitious: "Gather ye rosebuds while ye may" is only the most famous of his statements on the swift passage of time.

Then there is the pious verse in *His Noble Numbers*. Only a little of it is very good. He has none of the seemingly wild intensity of John Donne, none of the immaculately quiet intensity of George Herbert: their religious poems are light-years beyond Herrick's. I see no mystery here. Robert Herrick shows no evidence of having been a passionately religious man. No spiritual wrestling or spiritual agony enforces his verse. Like Andrew Marvell, he is very much aware of "vast eternitie," yet he is rather given to thanking God for creature comforts—even in a "living" grave. He does not tear one to pieces as Donne and Herbert can. At his best, his religious verse is beguiling: "Here a little child I stand," and a few other felicitous moments.

But, pious or impious, what a God's plenty of beautiful poems are in this yield!

One is almost loath to comment on it. Why analyze the rose? J. Max Patrick says, "analysis is possible but extraneous." Herrick is remindful of a later, by no means dissimilar, and also very great poet, Robert Burns. In *The Well Wrought Urn* Cleanth Brooks puts the case thus in an explication of the magnificent "Corinna's Going a-Maying": " 'What does the poem communicate?' is badly asked. It is not that the poem communicates nothing. Precisely the contrary. The poem communicates so much and communicates it so richly and with such delicate qualifications that the thing communicated is mauled and distorted if we attempt to convey it by any vehicle less subtle than that of the poem itself." His most perfect poems are brief lyrics. Yet his comparatively long poems must be read with admiration for his fine craftsmanship in the shaping and control of rhyme and stanza form and for the grace of detail.

Robert Herrick's reputation has mounted steadily higher since his rediscovery at the beginning of the nineteenth century. And I suppose his attraction to our age is that such poetry as his could not possibly be written in our time. (It has, alas, been attempted.) It is the music of another age, another world, so superbly written that it moves us; foreign to us, yet not remote; different from any authentic music of ours, yet thrilling still.

But enough! Here is a poet whose vanity even is charming: he expresses a wish to God to spend his own latter years "Reading thy Bible, and my book"; and we grow the fonder of him because he is so naked. Let us keep his counsel: "to live merrily and to trust to good verses." Let us walk now through this gate into Herrick's eternal meadow.

Winfield Townley Scott

I

HESPERIDES

The Argument of His Book

⚜

I SING of brooks, of blossoms, birds, and bowers:
Of April, May, of June and July-flowers.
I sing of May-poles, hock-carts, wassails, wakes,
Of bridegrooms, brides, and of their bridal-cakes.
I write of youth, of love, and have access
By these, to sing of cleanly wantonness.
I sing of dews, of rains, and piece by piece
Of balm, of oil, of spice and ambergris.
I sing of times trans-shifting; and I write
How roses first came red, and lilies white.
I write of groves, of twilights, and I sing
The court of Mab, and of the fairy king.
I write of Hell; I sing (and ever shall)
Of Heaven, and hope to have it after all.

Another to His Book

⚜

TO READ my book the virgin shy
May blush (while Brutus standeth by):
But when he's gone, read through what's writ,
And never stain a cheek for it.

The Night Piece, to Julia

HER EYES the glowworm lend thee,
The shooting stars attend thee;
    And the elves also,
    Whose little eyes glow
Like sparks of fire, befriend thee.

No will-o'-the-wisp mislight thee,
Nor snake or slow-worm bite thee:
    But on, on thy way
    Not making a stay,
Since ghost there's none to affright thee.

Let not the dark thee cumber,
What though the moon does slumber?
    The stars of the night
    Will lend thee their light
Like tapers clear without number.

Then, Julia, let me woo thee,
Thus, thus to come unto me:
    And when I shall meet
    Thy silvery feet,
My soul I'll pour into thee.

A Song to the Masters

*

COME down, and dance ye in the toil
   Of pleasures, to a heat;
But if to moisture, let the oil
   Of roses be your sweat.

Not only to yourselves assume
   These sweets, but let them fly;
From this to that, and so perfume
   Even all the standers by.

As goddess Isis (when she went,
   Or glided through the street)
Made all that touched her with her scent,
   And whom she touched, turn sweet.

Delight in Disorder

A SWEET disorder in the dress
Kindles in clothes a wantonness:
A lawn about the shoulders thrown
Into a fine distraction:
An erring lace, which here and there
Enthralls the crimson stomacher:
A cuff neglectful, and thereby
Ribbons to flow confusedly:
A winning wave (deserving note)
In the tempestuous petticoat:
A careless shoestring, in whose tie
I see a wild civility:
Does more bewitch me than when art
Is too precise in every part.

Discontents in Devon

❢

MORE discontents I never had
   Since I was born, than here;
Where I have been and still am sad,
   In this dull Devonshire:
Yet justly too I must confess
   I ne'er invented such
Ennobled numbers for the press
   Than where I loathed so much.

Cherry-Ripe

❢

CHERRY-RIPE, ripe, ripe, I cry,
Full and fair ones, come and buy:
If so be you ask me where
They do grow, I answer: There,
Where my Julia's lips do smile;
There's the land, or cherry-isle,
Whose plantations fully show
All the year where cherries grow.

To the Reverend Shade of His Religious Father

THAT for seven lusters I did never come
To do the rites to thy religious tomb;
That neither hair was cut or true tears shed
By me, o'er thee (as justments to the dead),
Forgive, forgive me; since I did not know
Whether thy bones had here their rest or no.
But now 'tis known, behold, behold, I bring
Unto thy ghost, the effused offering:
And look, what smallage, night-shade, cypress, yew,
Unto the shades have been or now are due,
Here I devote; and something more than so;
I come to pay a debt of birth I owe.
Thou gav'st me life (but mortal); for that one
Favor, I'll make full satisfaction;
For my life mortal, rise from out thy hearse,
And take a life immortal from my verse.

To Laurels

＊

A FUNERAL stone,
Or verse I covet none;
But only crave
Of you, that I may have
A sacred laurel springing from my grave:
Which being seen,
Blest with perpetual green,
May grow to be
Not so much called a tree,
As the eternal monument of me.

To Critics

＊

I'LL WRITE, because I'll give
You critics means to live:
For should I not supply
The cause, the effect would die.

Divination by a Daffodil

WHEN a daffodil I see,
Hanging down his head towards me;
Guess I may what I must be:
First, I shall decline my head;
Secondly, I shall be dead;
Lastly, safely buried.

Upon Julia's Ribbon

AS SHOWS the air when with a rainbow graced,
So smiles that ribbon about my Julia's waist:
Or like—nay, 'tis that zonulet of love,
Wherein all pleasures of the world are wove.

His Parting from Mistress Dorothy Keneday

WHEN I did go from thee, I felt that smart,
Which bodies do, when souls from them depart.
Thou did'st not mind it; though thou mightest see
Me turned to tears; yet did'st not weep for me.
'Tis true, I kissed thee; but I could not hear
Thee spend a sigh to accompany my tear.
Methought 'twas strange, that thou so hard shouldst prove,
Whose heart, whose hand, whose every part spake love.
Prithee (lest maids should censure thee) but say
Thou shed'st one tear whenas I went away;
And that will please me somewhat: though I know,
And love will swear it, my dearest did not so.

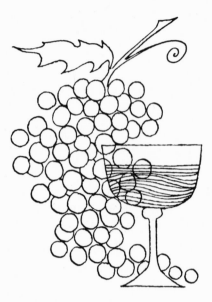

His Farewell to Sack

Farewell thou thing, time-past so known, so dear
To me, as blood to life and spirit: near,
Nay, thou more near than kindred, friend, man, wife,
Male to the female, soul to body: life
To quick action, or the warm soft side
Of the resigning yet resisting bride.
The kiss of virgins; first-fruits of the bed;
Soft speech, smooth touch, the lips, the maidenhead:

These and a thousand sweets could never be
So near, or dear, as thou wast once to me.
O thou the drink of gods and angels! wine
That scatterest spirit and lust; whose purest shine
More radiant than the summer's sunbeam shows;
Each way illustrious, brave; and like to those
Comets we see by night, whose shagged portents
Foretell the coming of some dire events:
Or some full flame, which with a pride aspires,
Throwing about his wild and active fires.
'Tis thou, above nectar, O divinest soul!
(Eternal in thyself) that canst control
That which subverts whole nature, grief and care,
Vexation of the mind, and damned despair.
'Tis thou alone who with thy mystic fan
Work'st more than wisdom, art, or nature can,
To rouse the sacred madness; and awake
The frost-bound blood and spirits; and to make
Them frantic with thy raptures, flashing through
The soul like lightning, and as active too.
'Tis not Apollo can, or those thrice three
Castalian sisters, sing if wanting thee.
Horace, Anacreon, both had lost their fame
Had'st thou not filled them with thy fire and flame.
Phoebean splendor! and thou Thespian spring!
Of which sweet swans must drink before they sing
Their true-paced numbers and their holy lays,
Which makes them worthy cedar and the bays.

But why? why longer do I gaze upon
Thee with the eye of admiration?
Since I must leave thee; and enforced must say
To all thy witching beauties, go, away.
But if thy whimpering looks do ask me why?
Then know that nature bids thee go, not I.
'Tis her erroneous self has made a brain
Uncapable of such a sovereign
As is thy powerful self. Prithee not smile,
Or smile more inly, lest thy looks beguile
My vows denounced in zeal, which thus much show thee
That I have sworn but by thy looks to know thee.
Let others drink thee freely, and desire
Thee and their lips espoused; while I admire
And love thee, but not taste thee. Let my Muse
Fail of thy former helps, and only use
Her unadulterate strength: what's done by me
Hereafter, shall smell of the lamp not thee.

Some Comfort in Calamity

TO CONQUERED men, some comfort 'tis to fall
By the hand of him who is the general.

The Vision

❧

SITTING alone (as one forsook)
Close by the silver-shedding brook,
With hands held up to love, I wept,
And after sorrows spent I slept:
Then in a vision I did see
A glorious form appear to me:
A virgin's face she had, her dress
Was like a sprightly Spartaness.
A silver bow with green silk strung
Down from her comely shoulders hung:
And as she stood, the wanton air
Dandled the ringlets of her hair.
Her legs were such Diana shows
When tucked up she a-hunting goes,
With buskins shortened to descry
The happy dawning of her thigh:
Which when I saw I made access
To kiss that tempting nakedness:
But she forbade me with a wand
Of myrtle she had in her hand:
And chiding me said, Hence, remove,
Herrick, thou art too coarse to love.

Tears Are Tongues

WHEN Julia chid, I stood as mute the while
As is the fish or tongueless crocodile.
Air coined to words my Julia could not hear;
But she could see each eye to stamp a tear:
By which my angry mistress might descry
Tears are the noble language of the eye.
And when true love of words is destitute,
The eyes by tears speak while the tongue is mute.

His Protestation to Perilla

NOONDAY and midnight shall at once be seen:
Trees at one time shall be both sere and green:
Fire and water shall together lie
In one self-sweet-conspiring sympathy:
Summer and winter shall at one time show
Ripe ears of corn and up to the ears in snow:
Seas shall be sandless, fields devoid of grass:
Shapeless the world (as when all chaos was)
Before, my dear Perilla, I will be
False to my vow, or fall away from thee.

A Ring Presented to Julia

JULIA, I bring
To thee this ring,
Made for thy finger fit;
To show by this,
That our love is
(Or should be) like to it.

Close though it be,
The joint is free:
So when love's yoke is on,
It must not gall
Or fret at all
With hard oppression.

But it must play
Still either way;
And be, too, such a yoke
As not too wide
To over-slide
Or be too strait to choke.

So we, who bear
This beam, must rear
Ourselves to such a height

As that the stay
Of either may
Create the burden light.

And as this round
Is nowhere found
To flaw, or else to sever:
So let our love
As endless prove,
And pure as gold forever.

To Dianeme

SWEET, be not proud of those two eyes
Which star-like sparkle in their skies:
Nor be you proud that you can see
All hearts your captives: yours, yet free.
Be you not proud of that rich hair
Which wantons with the love-sick air:
Whenas that ruby which you wear,
Sunk from the tip of your soft ear,
Will last to be a precious stone
When all your world of beauty's gone.

Corinna's Going a-Maying

GET UP, get up for shame! The blooming morn
Upon her wings presents the god unshorn.
      See how Aurora throws her fair
      Fresh-quilted colors through the air:
      Get up, sweet slug-a-bed, and see
      The dew bespangling herb and tree.
Each flower has wept and bowed toward the east
An hour since; yet you not dressed,
      Nay! not so much as out of bed?
      When all the birds have matins said,
      And sung their thankful hymns: 'tis sin,
      Nay, profanation to keep in,
Whenas a thousand virgins on this day
Spring, sooner than the lark, to fetch in May.

Rise and put on your foliage, and be seen
To come forth, like the springtime, fresh and green,
      And sweet as Flora. Take no care
      For jewels for your gown or hair:
      Fear not, the leaves will strew
      Gems in abundance upon you:
Besides, the childhood of the day has kept,
Against you come, some orient pearls unwept:
      Come and receive them while the light

Hangs on the dew-locks of the night,
And Titan on the eastern hill
Retires himself, or else stands still
Till you come forth. Wash, dress, be brief in praying:
Few beads are best when once we go a-Maying.

Come, my Corinna, come; and coming, mark
How each field turns a street, each street a park
     Made green and trimmed with trees: see how
     Devotion gives each house a bough
     Or branch: each porch, each door, ere this,
     An ark, a tabernacle is
Made up of white-thorn neatly interwove;
As if here were those cooler shades of love.
     Can such delights be in the street
     And open fields, and we not see't?
     Come, we'll abroad; and let's obey
     The proclamation made for May,
And sin no more, as we have done, by staying;
But my Corinna, come, let's go a-Maying.

There's not a budding boy or girl this day
But is got up and gone to bring in May.
     A deal of youth, ere this, is come
     Back, and with white-thorn laden home.
     Some have dispatched their cakes and cream
     Before that we have left to dream:
And some have wept and wooed and plighted troth

And chose their priest, ere we can cast off sloth:
> Many a green-gown has been given,
> Many a kiss, both odd and even;
> Many a glance too has been sent
> From out the eye, love's firmament;
Many a jest told of the keys betraying
This night, and locks picked, yet we are not a-Maying.

Come, let us go while we are in our prime,
And take the harmless folly of the time.
> We shall grow old apace, and die
> Before we know our liberty.
> Our life is short, and our days run
> As fast away as does the sun:
And as a vapor, or a drop of rain
Once lost, can ne'er be found again:
> So when or you or I are made
> A fable, song, or fleeting shade,
> All love, all liking, all delight
> Lies drowned with us in endless night.
Then while time serves, and we are but decaying,
Come, my Corinna, come, let's go a-Maying.

An Ode to Master Endymion Porter,
upon His Brother's Death*

NOT ALL thy flushing suns are set,
            Herrick, as yet:
Nor doth this far-drawn hemisphere
Frown and look sullen everywhere.
Days may conclude in nights; and suns may rest,
    As dead, within the west,
Yet the next morn reguild the fragrant east.

*I.e., the death of *Herrick's* brother.

Alas for me! that I have lost
                    Even all a'most:
Sunk is my sight; set is my sun;
And all the loom of life undone:
The staff, the elm, the prop, the sheltering wall
            Whereon my vine did crawl,
Now, now blown down; needs must the old stock fall.

Yet, Porter, while thou keep'st alive,
                    In death I thrive:
And like a phoenix re-aspire
From out my nard and funeral fire.
And as I preen my feathered youth, so I
            Do marvel how I could die
When I had thee, my chief preserver, by.

I'm up, I'm up, and bless that hand
                    Which makes me stand
Now as I do; and but for thee,
I must confess, I could not be.
The debt is paid: for he who doth resign
            Thanks to the generous vine,
Invites fresh grapes to fill his press with wine.

The Lily in a Crystal

YOU HAVE beheld a smiling rose
    When virgins' hands have drawn
    O'er it a cobweb lawn:
And here, you see, this lily shows,
    Tombed in a crystal stone,
More fair in this transparent case
    Than when it grew alone
    And had but single grace.

You see how cream but naked is,
    Nor dances in the eye
    Without a strawberry:
Or some fine tincture, like to this,
    Which draws the sight thereto,
More by that wantoning with it,
    Than when the paler hue
    No mixture did admit.

You see how amber through the streams
    More gently strokes the sight
    With some concealed delight,
Than when he darts his radiant beams
    Into the boundless air:
Where either too much light his worth

Doth all at once impair,
Or set it little forth.

Put purple grapes or cherries in-
To glass, and they will send
More beauty to commend
Them, from that clean and subtle skin,
Than if they naked stood
And had no other pride at all,
But their own flesh and blood
And tinctures natural.

Thus lily, rose, grape, cherry, cream,
And strawberry do stir
More love when they transfer
A weak, a soft, a broken beam,
Than if they should discover
At full their proper excellence,
Without some skein cast over
To juggle with the sense.

Thus let this crystalled lily be
A rule, how far to teach
Your nakedness must reach:
And that, no further than we see
Those glaring colors laid
By art's wise hand, but to this end

They should obey a shade,
Lest they too far extend.

So though you are white as swan or snow,
And have the power to move
A world of men to love:
Yet when your lawns and silks shall flow
And that white cloud divide
Into a doubtful twilight: then,
Then will your hidden pride
Raise greater fires in men.

Impossibilities to His Friend

MY FAITHFUL friend, if you can see
The fruit to grow upon the tree:
If you can see the color come
Into the blushing pear or plum:
If you can see the water grow
To cakes of ice or flakes of snow:
If you can see that drop of rain,
Lost in the wild sea, once again:
If you can see how dreams do creep
Into the brain by easy sleep:
Then there is hope that you may see
Her love me once, who now hates me.

To Live Merrily and to Trust to Good Verses

Now is the time for mirth;
  Nor cheek or tongue be dumb;
For with the flowery earth
  The golden pomp is come.

The golden pomp is come;
  For now each tree does wear,
Made of her pap and gum,
  Rich beads of amber here.

Now reigns the rose, and now
  The Arabian dew besmears
My uncontrollèd brow
  And my retorted hairs.

Homer, this health to thee,
  In sack of such a kind
That it would make thee see
  Though thou wert ne'er so blind.

Next, Virgil I'll call forth,
  To pledge this second health
In wine whose each cup's worth
  An Indian commonwealth.

A goblet next I'll drink
    To Ovid; and suppose,
Made he the pledge, he'd think
    The world had all one nose.

Then this immensive cup
    Of aromatic wine,
Catullus, I quaff up
    To that terse Muse of thine.

Wild I am now with heat;
    O Bacchus! cool thy rays!
Or, frantic, I shall eat
    Thy thyrse, and bite the bays.

Round, round, the roof does run;
    And, being ravished thus,
Come, I will drink a tun
    To my Propertius.

Now, to Tibullus next,
    This flood I drink to thee.
But stay; I see a text
    That this presents to me:

Behold, Tibullus lies
    Here burnt, whose small return

Of ashes scarce suffice
   To fill a little urn.

Trust to good verses, then;
   They only will aspire,
When pyramids, as men,
   Are lost in the funeral fire.

And when all bodies meet,
   In Lethe to be drowned,
Then only numbers sweet
   With endless life are crowned.

To the Virgins, to Make Much of Time

GATHER ye rosebuds while ye may,
    Old time is still a-flying:
And this same flower that smiles today,
    Tomorrow will be dying.

The glorious lamp of heaven, the sun,
    The higher he's a-getting,
The sooner will his race be run,
    And nearer he's to setting.

That age is best which is the first,
    When youth and blood are warmer;
But being spent, the worse, and worst
    Times still succeed the former.

Then be not coy, but use your time,
    And while ye may, go marry:
For having lost but once your prime,
    You may forever tarry.

His Poetry His Pillar

ONLY a little more
  I have to write,
  Then I'll give o'er
And bid the world Goodnight.

'Tis but a flying minute
  That I must stay,
  Or linger in it;
And then I must away.

O time that cuts down all!
  And scarce leaves here
  Memorial
Of any men that were.

How many lie forgot
  In vaults beneath?
  And piecemeal rot
Without a fame in death?

Behold this living stone,
  I rear for me,
  Ne'er to be thrown
Down, envious time, by thee.

Pillars let some set up
(If so they please)
Here is my hope,
And my *pyramides.*

A Meditation for His Mistress

⚘

YOU ARE a tulip seen today,
But (dearest) of so short a stay
That where you grew, scarce man can say.

You are a lovely July-flower,
Yet one rude wind, or ruffling shower,
Will force you hence (and in a hour).

You are a sparkling rose in the bud, ˙
Yet lost, ere that chaste flesh and blood
Can show where you or grew or stood.

You are a full-spread fair-set vine,
And can with tendrils love entwine,
Yet dried ere you distill your wine.

You are a balm enclosed well
In amber, or some crystal shell,
Yet lost ere you transfuse your smell.

You are a dainty violet,
Yet withered ere you can be set
Within the virgin's coronet.

You are the queen all flowers among,
But die you must (fair maid) ere long,
As he, the maker of this song.

Lyric for Legacies

GOLD I've none, for use or show,
Neither silver to bestow
At my death; but thus much know,
That each lyric here shall be
Of my love a legacy,
Left to all posterity.
Gentle friends, then do but please
To accept such coins as these
As my last remembrances.

To Music, to Becalm His Fever

CHARM me asleep, and melt me so
   With thy delicious numbers,
That being ravished, hence I go
   Away in easy slumbers.
      Ease my sick head,
      And make my bed,
Thou power that canst sever
      From me this ill,
      And quickly still:
      Though thou not kill
         My fever.

Thou sweetly canst convert the same
   From a consuming fire,
Into a gentle-licking flame,
   And make it thus expire.
      Then make me sweep
      My pains asleep
And give me such reposes,
      That I, poor I,
      May think thereby
      I love and die
         'Mongst roses.

Fall on me like a silent dew,
　　Or like those maiden showers
Which, by the peep of day, do strew
　　A baptim o'er the flowers.
　　　Melt, melt my pains
　　　With thy soft strains,
That having ease me given,
　　　With full delight
　　　I leave this light
　　　And take my flight
　　　For heaven.

To the Western Wind

SWEET western wind, whose luck it is,
　　Made rival with the air,
To give Perenna's lip a kiss,
　　And fan her wanton hair:

Bring me but one, I'll promise thee,
　　Instead of common showers,
Thy wings shall be embalmed by me,
　　And all beset with flowers.

To Primroses Filled with Morning Dew

✤

WHY do ye weep, sweet babes? can tears
     Speak grief in you,
     Who were but born
    Just as the modest morn
    Teemed her refreshing dew?
Alas you have not known that shower
     That mars a flower,
     Nor felt the unkind
    Breath of a blasting wind;
    Nor are ye worn with years;
     Or warped, as we,
     Who think it strange to see
Such pretty flowers (like to orphans young)
To speak by tears, before ye have a tongue.

Speak, whimpering younglings, and make known
     The reason why
     Ye droop and weep;
    Is it for want of sleep?
    Or childish lullaby?
Or that ye have not seen as yet
     The violet?
     Or brought a kiss
    From that sweetheart to this?

Apostrophe

No, no, this sorrow shown
　　By your tears shed,
　Would have this lecture read,
That things of greatest, so of meanest worth,
Conceived with grief are, and with tears brought forth.

To Anthea, Who May Command Him Anything

BID ME to live, and I will live
　　Thy protestant to be:
Or bid me love, and I will give
　　A loving heart to thee.

A heart as soft, a heart as kind,
　　A heart as sound and free,
As in the whole world thou canst find,
　　That heart I'll give to thee.

Bid that heart stay, and it will stay,
　　To honor thy decree:
Or bid it languish quite away,
　　And 't shall do so for thee.

Bid me to weep, and I will weep,
  While I have eyes to see:
And having none, yet I will keep
  A heart to weep for thee.

Bid me despair, and I'll despair
  Under that cypress tree:
Or bid me die, and I will dare
  Even death, to die for thee.

Thou art my life, my love, my heart,
  The very eyes of me:
And hast command of every part
  To live and die for thee.

Oberon's Feast

Shapcot! To thee the Fairy State
I with discretion dedicate.
Because thou prizest things that are
Curious and unfamiliar.
Take first the feast; these dishes gone,
We'll see the Fairy Court *anon.*

A little mushroom table spread,
After short prayers, they set on bread;
A moon-parched grain of purest wheat,
With some small glittering grit, to eat
His choice bits with; then in a trice
They make a feast less great than nice.
But all this while his eye is served,
We must not think his ear was starved:
But that there was in place to stir
His spleen, the chirring grasshopper,
The merry cricket, puling fly,
The piping gnat for minstrelsy.
And now, we must imagine first,
The elves present to quench his thirst
A pure seed-pearl of infant dew,

Brought and besweetened in a blue
And pregnant violet; which done,
His kitling eyes begin to run
Quite through the table, where he spies
The horns of papery butterflies,
Of which he eats, and tastes a little
Of what we call the cuckoo's spittle.
A little fuzzball-pudding stands
By, yet not blessed by his hands,
That was too coarse; but then forthwith
He ventures boldly on the pith
Of sugared rush, and eats the sag
And well bestrutted bee's sweet bag:
Gladding his palate with some store
Of emmet's eggs; what would he more?
But beards of mice, a newt's stewed thigh,
A bloated earwig, and a fly;
With the red-capped worm, that's shut
Within the concave of a nut,
Brown as his tooth. A little moth,
Late fattened in a piece of cloth:
With withered cherries; mandrakes' ears;
Mole's eyes; to these, the slain stag's tears;
The unctuous dewlaps of a snail;
The broke heart of a nightingale
O'er-come in music; with a wine
Ne'er ravished from the flattering vine,

But gently pressed from the soft side
Of the most sweet and dainty bride,
Brought in a dainty daisy, which
He fully quaffs up to bewitch
His blood to height; this done, commended
Grace by his priest. *The feast is ended.*

The Bell-Man

   ⚓

FROM noise of Scare-fires rest ye free,
From Murders—*Benedicite.*
From all mischances, that may fright
Your pleasing slumbers in the night:
Mercy secure ye all, and keep
The Goblin from ye, while ye sleep.
Past one o'clock, and almost two,
My Masters all, *Good day to you.*

To Daffodils

FAIR daffodils, we weep to see
  You haste away so soon:
As yet the early-rising sun
  Has not attained his noon.
            Stay, stay,
    Until the hasting day
                Has run
    But to the evensong;
And, having prayed together, we
    Will go with you along.

We have short time to stay, as you,
  We have as short a spring;
As quick a growth to meet decay,
  As you, or anything.
            We die,
    As your hours do, and dry
                Away,
    Like to the summer's rain;
Or as the pearls of morning's dew
    Ne'er to be found again.

The Bracelet to Julia

WHY I tie about thy wrist,
Julia, this my silken twist;
For what other reason is't,
But to show thee how in part
Thou my pretty captive art?
But thy bondslave is my heart.
'Tis but silk that bindeth thee;
Knap the thread, and thou art free:
But 'tis otherwise with me.
I am bound, and fast bound so,
That from thee I cannot go;
If I could, I would not so.

The Parting Verse, the Feast There Ended

LOATH to depart, but yet at last each one
Back must now go to his habitation:
Not knowing thus much, when we once do sever,
Whether or no that we shall meet here ever.
As for myself, since time a thousand cares
And griefs hath filed upon my silver hairs,
'Tis to be doubted whether I next year,
Or no, shall give ye a re-meeting here.
If die I must, then my last vow shall be,
You'll with a tear or two remember me,
Your sometime poet; but if fates do give
Me longer date and more fresh springs to live:
Oft as your field shall her old age renew,
Herrick shall make the meadow-verse for you.

His Lachrimae, or Mirth Turned to Mourning

♆

CALL me no more,
As heretofore,
The music of a feast;
Since now (alas)
The mirth, that was
In me, is dead or ceased.

Before I went
To banishment
Into the loathèd west,
I could rehearse
A lyric verse
And speak it with the best.

But time (Ai me)
Has laid, I see,
My organ fast asleep;
And turned my voice
Into the noise
Of those that sit and weep.

The Mad Maid's Song

⚘

GOOD MORROW to the day so fair;
  Good morning, sir, to you:
Good morrow to mine own torn hair
  Bedabbled with the dew.

Good morning to the primrose too;
  Good morrow to each maid
That will with flowers the tomb bestrew
  Wherein my love is laid.

Ah woe is me, woe, woe is me,
  Alack and welladay!
For pity, sir, find out that bee
  Which bore my love away.

I'll seek him in your bonnet brave,
  I'll seek him in your eyes;
Nay, now I think they have made his grave
  In the bed of strawberries.

I'll seek him there; I know, ere this,
  The cold, cold earth doth shake him;
But I will go or send a kiss
  By you, sir, to awake him.

Pray hurt him not; though he be dead,
   He knows well who do love him,
And who with green turfs rear his head,
   And who do rudely move him.

He's soft and tender (pray take heed)
   With bands of cowslips bind him;
And bring him home, but 'tis decreed
   That I shall never find him.

Upon Julia's Unlacing Herself

TELL if thou canst (and truly) whence doth come
This camphor, storax, spikenard, galbanum:
These musks, these ambers, and those other smells
(Sweet as the vestry of the oracles).
I'll tell thee: when my Julia did unlace
Her silken bodice but a breathing space,
The passive air such odor then assumed
As when to Jove great Juno goes perfumed:
Whose pure immortal body doth transmit
A scent that fills both heaven and earth with it.

The Poet Loves a Mistress, But Not to Marry

I DO NOT love to wed
Though I do like to woo;
And for a maidenhead
I'll beg, and buy it too.

I'll praise and I'll approve
Those maids that never vary;
And fervently I'll love,
But yet I would not marry.

I'll hug, I'll kiss, I'll play,
And cock-like, hens I'll tread,
And sport it any way
But in the bridal bed.

For why? that man is poor
Who hath but one of many;
But crowned he is with store,
That single may have any.

Why then, say, what is he
(To freedom so unknown)
Who having two or three,
Will be content with one?

To Daisies, Not to Shut So Soon

SHUT NOT so soon; the dull-eyed night
    Has not as yet begun
To make a seizure on the light,
    Or to seal up the sun.

No marigolds yet closed are;
    No shadows great appear;
Nor doth the early shepherd's star
    Shine like a spangle here.

Stay but till my Julia close
    Her life-begetting eye,
And let the whole world then dispose
    Itself to live or die.

To Œnone

WHAT conscience, say, is it in thee,
  When I a heart had one,
To take away that heart from me,
  And to retain thy own?

For shame or pity now incline
  To play a loving part;
Either to send me kindly thine,
  Or give me back my heart.

Covet not both; but if thou dost
  Resolve to part with neither,
Why, yet to show that thou art just,
  Take me and mine together!

To Blossoms

FAIR pledges of a fruitful tree,
　　Why do you fall so fast?
　　Your date is not so past
But you may stay yet here awhile,
　　To blush and gently smile
　　　　And go at last.

What, were you born to be
　　An hour or half's delight,
　　And so to bid goodnight?
'Twas pity nature brought you forth
　　Merely to show your worth,
　　　　And lose you quite.

But you are lovely leaves, where we
　　May read how soon things have
　　Their end, though ne'er so brave:
And after they have shown their pride
　　Like you awhile, they glide
　　　　Into the grave.

Upon His Departure Hence

*

Thus I
Pass by
And die:
As one
Unknown
And gone;
I'm made
A shade
And laid
In the grave,
There have
My cave.
Where tell
I dwell.
Farewell.

To Sir Clipseby Crew

SINCE to the country first I came,
I have lost my former flame
And, methinks, I not inherit,
As I did, my ravished spirit.
If I write a verse or two,
'Tis with very much ado;
In regard I want that wine
Which should conjure up a line.
Yet, though now of Muse bereft,
I have still the manners left
For to thank you, noble Sir,
For those gifts you do confer
Upon him, who only can
Be in prose a grateful man.

His Winding Sheet

COME thou, who art the wine and wit
  Of all I've writ:
The grace, the glory, and the best
  Piece of the rest.
Thou art of what I did intend
  The all and end.
And what was made, was made to meet
  Thee, thee my sheet.
Come then, and be to my chaste side
  Both bed and bride.
We two as relics left will have
  One rest, one grave.
And hugging close, we will not fear
  Lust entering here,
Where all desires are dead, or cold
  As is the mold,
And all affections are forgot,
  Or trouble not.
Here, here the slaves and prisoners be
  From shackles free,
And weeping widows long oppressed
  Do here find rest.
The wrongèd client ends his laws
  Here, and his cause.

Here those long suits of Chancery lie
        Quiet, or die;
And all Star-chamber bills do cease,
        Or hold their peace.
Here needs no Court for our Request,
        Where all are best:
All wise, all equal, and all just
        Alike in the dust.
Nor need we here to fear the frown
        Of Court or Crown.
Where fortune bears no sway o'er things,
        There all are kings.
In this securer place we'll keep,
        As lulled asleep;
Or for a little time we'll lie,
        As robes laid by,
To be another day re-worn,
        Turned, but not torn.
Or like old testaments engrossed,
        Locked up, not lost;
And for a while lie here concealed,
        To be revealed
Next at that great Platonic year,
        And then meet here.

Upon His Gray Hairs

❦

FLY me not, though I be gray,
Lady, this I know you'll say;
Better look the roses red
When with white commingled.
Black your hairs are; mine are white;
This begets the more delight,
When things meet most opposite:
As in pictures we descry
Venus standing Vulcan by.

To Marigolds

❦

GIVE WAY, and be you ravished by the sun,
(And hang the head whenas the act is done);
Spread as he spreads; wax less as he does wane;
And as he shuts, close up to maids again.

His Content in the Country

HERE, here I live with what my board
Can with the smallest cost afford.
Though ne'er so mean the viands be,
They well content my Prew and me.
Or pea, or bean, or wort, or beet,
Whatever comes, content makes sweet.
Here we rejoice because no rent
We pay for our poor tenement
Wherein we rest, and never fear
The landlord or the usurer.
The quarter-day does ne'er affright
Our peaceful slumbers in the night.
We eat our own, and batten more
Because we feed on no man's score,
But pity those whose flanks grow great,
Swelled with the lard of others' meat.
We bless our fortunes when we see
Our own beloved privacy;
And like our living, where we are known
To very few, or else to none.

The Fairies

⚜

IF YOU will with Mab find grace,
Set each platter in his place:
Rake the fire up, and get
Water in, ere sun be set.
Wash your pails, and cleanse your dairies:
Sluts are loathsome to the fairies.
Sweep your house: who doth not so,
Mab will pinch her by the toe.

Upon the Troublesome Times

❧

O! TIMES most bad,
Without the scope
Of hope
Of better to be had!

Where shall I go,
Or whither run
To shun
This public overthrow?

No places are
(This I am sure)
Secure
In this our wasting war.

Some storms we have passed;
Yet we must all
Down fall,
And perish at the last.

Pains without Profit

A LONG life's day I've taken pains
For very little or no gains:
The evening's come; here now I'll stop,
And work no more, but shut up shop.

His Prayer to Ben Jonson

WHEN I a verse shall make,
Know I have prayed thee,
For old religion's sake,
Saint Ben, to aid me.

Make the way smooth for me
When I, thy Herrick,
Honoring thee, on my knee
Offer my lyric.

Candles I'll give to thee,
And a new altar;
And thou, Saint Ben, shall be
Writ in my psalter.

The Bad Season Makes the Poet Sad

Dull to my self, and almost dead to these
My many fresh and fragrant mistresses:
Lost to all music now, since everything
Puts on the semblance here of sorrowing.
Sick is the land to the heart, and doth endure
More dangerous faintings by her desperate cure.
But if that golden age would come again
And Charles here rule, as he before did reign;
If smooth and unperplexed the seasons were,
As when the sweet Maria livèd here;
I should delight to have my curls half drowned
In Tyrian dews, and head with roses crowned;
And once more yet, ere I am laid out dead,
Knock at a star with my exalted head.

To Silvia to Wed

LET US (though late) at last (my Silvia) wed;
And loving lie in one devoted bed.
Thy watch may stand, my minutes fly posthaste;
No sound calls back the year that once is past.
Then sweetest Silvia, let's no longer stay;
True love, we know, precipitates delay.
Away with doubts, all scruples hence remove;
No man at one time can be wise and love.

To Sir Clipseby Crew

⁕

GIVE ME wine and give me meat,
To create in me a heat,
That my pulses high may beat.

Cold and hunger never yet
Could a noble verse beget,
But your bowls with sack replete.

Give me these (my Knight) and try
In a minute's space how I
Can run mad, and prophesy.

Then if any piece proves new
And rare, I'll say (my dearest Crew)
It was all inspired by you.

Glory

☙

I MAKE no haste to have my Numbers read.
Seldom comes glory till a man be dead.

Poets

☙

WANTONS we are; and though our words be such,
Our lives do differ from our lines by much.

To His Lovely Mistresses

ONE NIGHT in the year, my dearest beauties, come
And bring those dew-drink offerings to my tomb.
When thence you see my reverend ghost to rise
And there to lick the effusèd sacrifice,
Though paleness be the livery I wear,
Look you not wan or colorless for fear.
Trust me I will not hurt you or once show
The least grim look, or cast a frown on you;
Nor shall the tapers when I'm there burn blue.
This I may do (perhaps) as I glide by,
Cast on my girls a glance, and loving eye;
Or fold my arms and sigh, because I've lost
The world so soon, and in it, you the most.
Than these, no fears more on your fancies fall,
Though then I smile and speak no words at all.

The Hag

THE HAG is astride,
This night for to ride;
The devil and she together:
Through thick, and through thin,
Now out, and then in,
Though ne'er so foul be the weather.

A thorn or a burr
She takes for a spur:
With a lash of a bramble she rides now,
Through brakes and through briars,
O'er ditches, and mires,
She follows the spirit that guides now.

No beast, for his food,
Dares now range the wood;
But hushed in his lair he lies lurking:
While mischiefs, by these,
On land and on seas,
At noon of night are a-working.

The storm will arise,
And trouble the skies;
This night, and more for the wonder,

The ghost from the tomb
Affrighted shall come,
Called out by the clap of the thunder.

To Electra

⚘

I DARE not ask a kiss;
I dare not beg a smile;
Lest having that, or this,
I might grow proud the while.

No, no, the utmost share
Of my desire shall be
Only to kiss that air
That lately kissed thee.

Once Seen, and No More

⁂

THOUSANDS each day pass by which we,
Once past and gone, no more shall see.

Laxare Fibulam

⁂

TO LOOSE the button is no less
Than to cast off all bashfulness.

His Grange, or Private Wealth

THOUGH clock,
To tell how night draws hence, I've none,
A cock
I have, to sing how day draws on.
I have
A maid (my Prew) by good luck sent,
To save
That little, fates me gave or lent.
A hen
I keep, which creeking day by day,
Tells when
She goes her long white egg to lay.
A goose
I have, which, with a jealous ear,
Lets loose
Her tongue, to tell what danger's near.
A lamb
I keep (tame) with my morsels fed,
Whose dam
An orphan left him (lately dead).
A cat
I keep, that plays about my house,
Grown fat
With eating many a miching mouse.

To these
A Trasy* I do keep, whereby
I please
The more my rural privacy:
Which are
But toys to give my heart some ease.
Where care
None is, slight things do lightly please.

*Trasy. His spaniel. (Herrick's note)

A Ternary of Littles, upon a Pipkin of Jelly Sent to a Lady

A LITTLE saint best fits a little shrine,
A little prop best fits a little vine:
As my small cruse best fits my little wine.

A little seed best fits a little soil,
A little trade best fits a little toil:
As my small jar best fits my little oil.

A little bin best fits a little bread,
A little garland fits a little head:
As my small stuff best fits my little shed.

A little hearth best fits a little fire,
A little chapel fits a little choir:
As my small bell best fits my little spire.

A little stream best fits a little boat,
A little lead best fits a little float:
As my small pipe best fits my little note.

A little meat best fits a little belly,
As sweetly, lady, give me leave to tell ye,
This little pipkin fits this little jelly.

Lovers How They Come and Part

·

A GYGES ring they bear about them still,
To be, and not, seen when and where they will.
They tread on clouds, and though they sometimes fall,
They fall like dew, but make no noise at all.
So silently they one to the other come,
As colors steal into the pear or plum,
And air-like, leave no pression to be seen
Where'er they met, or parting place has been.

Upon Julia's Clothes

·

WHENAS in silks my Julia goes,
Then, then (methinks) how sweetly flows
That liquefaction of her clothes.

Next, when I cast my eyes and see
That brave vibration each way free,
O how that glittering taketh me!

Upon Prew His Maid

※

In this little urn is laid
Prewdence Baldwin (once my maid)
From whose happy spark here let
Spring the purple violet.

Burial

※

Man may want land to live in; but for all,
Nature finds some place for burial.

The Amber Bead

I saw a fly within a bead
Of amber cleanly burièd:
The urn was little, but the room
More rich than Cleopatra's tomb.

To Julia, in Her Dawn or Daybreak

By the next kindling of the day
    My Julia thou shalt see,
Ere *Ave-Mary* thou canst say
    I'll come and visit thee.

Yet ere thou counselest with thy glass,
    Appear thou to my eyes
As smooth and naked as she that was
    The prime of paradise.

If blush thou must, then blush thou through
    A lawn, that thou mayst look
As purest pearls, or pebbles do
    When peeping through a brook.

As lilies shrined in crystal, so
    Do thou to me appear;
Or damask roses, when they grow
    To sweet acquaintance there.

Upon a Maid

∗

HERE she lies in bed of spice
Fair as Eve in paradise:
For her beauty it was such
Poets could not praise too much.
Virgins come, and in a ring
Her supremest requiem sing;
Then depart, but see you tread
Lightly, lightly o'er the dead.

An Ode for Ben Jonson

AH BEN!
Say how or when
Shall we thy guests
Meet at those lyric feasts
Made at the Sun,
The Dog, the triple Tunne?
Where we such clusters had
As made us nobly wild, not mad;
And yet each verse of thine
Outdid the meat, outdid the frolic wine.

My Ben
Or come again:
Or send to us
Thy wit's great overplus;
But teach us yet
Wisely to husband it,
Lest we that talent spend:
And having once brought to an end
That precious stock, the store
Of such a wit the world should have no more.

The Present Time Best Pleaseth

PRAISE they that will times past, I joy to see
My self now live: this age best pleaseth me.

Upon Love, by Way of Question and Answer

I BRING ye love: *Quest.* What will love do?
    Ans. Like and dislike ye.
I bring ye love: *Quest.* What will love do?
    Ans. Stroke ye to strike ye.
I bring ye love: *Quest.* What will love do?
    Ans. Love will befool ye.
I bring ye love: *Quest.* What will love do?
    Ans. Heat ye to cool ye.
I bring ye love: *Quest.* What will love do?
    Ans. Love gifts will send ye.
I bring ye love: *Quest.* What will love do?
    Ans. Stock ye to spend ye.
I bring ye love: *Quest.* What will love do?
    Ans. Love will fulfill ye.
I bring ye love: *Quest.* What will love do?
    Ans. Kiss ye, to kill ye.

Charm

⁂

In the morning when ye rise
Wash your hands, and cleanse your eyes.
Next be sure ye have a care,
To disperse the water far.
For as far as that doth light,
So far keeps the evil Spright.

Another

⁂

If ye fear to be affrighted
When ye are (by chance) benighted,
In your pocket for a trust
Carry nothing but a crust:
For that holy piece of bread
Charms the danger, and the dread.

His Covenant or Protestation to Julia

WHY dost thou wound and break my heart?
As if we should forever part?
Hast thou not heard an oath from me,
After a day, or two, or three,
I would come back and live with thee?
Take, if thou dost distrust that vow,
This second protestation now.
Upon thy cheek that spangled tear
Which sits as dew of roses there:
That tear shall scarce be dried before
I'll kiss the threshold of thy door.
Then weep not, sweet, but thus much know,
I'm half returned before I go.

To His Girls Who Would Have Him Sportful

Alas, I can't; for tell me how
Can I be gamesome, aged now.
Besides you see me daily grow
Here winter-like to frost and snow.
And I ere long, my girls, shall see
You quake for cold to look on me.

His Last Request to Julia

I have been wanton and too bold, I fear,
To chafe o'er much the virgin's cheek or ear:
Beg for my pardon, Julia; he doth win
Grace from the gods. who's sorry for his sin.
That done, my Julia—dearest Julia—come
And go with me to choose my burial room:
My fates are ended; when thy Herrick dies,
Clasp thou his book, then close thou up his eyes.

To His Book

Go thou forth my book, though late;
Yet be timely fortunate.
It may chance good luck may send
Thee a kinsman or a friend
That may harbor thee when I
With my fates neglected lie.
If thou knowest not where to dwell,
See, the fire's by: *Farewell.*

To his book's end this last line he'd have placed:
Jocund his muse was, but his life was chaste.

II

HIS NOBLE NUMBERS

His Confession

.*.

LOOK how our foul days do exceed our fair;
And as our bad, more than our good works are:
Even so those lines, penned by my wanton wit,
Treble the number of these good I've writ.
Things precious are least numerous: men are prone
To do ten bad, for one good action.

To God

.*.

Do with me, God! as Thou didst deal with John
Who writ that heavenly *Revelation*;
Let me, like him, first cracks of thunder hear,
Then let the harp's enchantments strike my ear.
Here give me thorns; there, in thy kingdom, set
Upon my head the golden coronet;
There give me day; but here my dreadful night:
My sackcloth here; but there my stole of white.

His Ejaculation to God

MY GOD! look on me with thine eye
Of pity, not of scrutiny;
For if thou dost, thou then shalt see
Nothing but loathsome sores in me.
O then! for mercy's sake, behold
These my eruptions manifold;
And heal me with thy look or touch:
But if thou wilt not deign so much
Because I'm odious in thy sight,
Speak but the word and cure me quite.

His Litany, to The Holy Spirit

*

In the hour of my distress,
When temptations me oppress,
And when I my sins confess,
　　　　Sweet Spirit comfort me!

When I lie within my bed,
Sick in heart and sick in head,
And with doubts discomforted,
　　　　Sweet Spirit comfort me!

When the house doth sigh and weep,
And the world is drowned in sleep,
Yet my eyes the watch do keep,
　　　　Sweet Spirit comfort me!

When the artless doctor sees
No one hope, but of his fees,
And his skill runs on the lees,
　　　　Sweet Spirit comfort me!

When his potion and his pill,
His, or none, or little skill,
Meet for nothing but to kill,
　　　　Sweet Spirit comfort me!

When the passing-bell doth toll,
And the Furies in a shole
Come to fright a parting soul,
   Sweet Spirit comfort me!

When the tapers now burn blue,
And the comforters are few,
And that number more than true,
   Sweet Spirit comfort me!

When the priest his last hath prayed,
And I nod to what is said,
'Cause my speech is now decayed,
   Sweet Spirit comfort me!

When (God knows) I'm tossed about,
Either with despair or doubt,
Yet before the glass be out,
   Sweet Spirit comfort me!

When the Tempter me pursu'th
With the sins of all my youth,
And half damns me with untruth,
   Sweet Spirit comfort me!

When the flames and hellish cries
Fright my ears and fright my eyes,
And all terrors me surprise,
   Sweet Spirit comfort me!

When the Judgment is revealed,
And that opened which was sealed,
When to Thee I have appealed,
      Sweet Spirit comfort me!

Cockcrow

BELLMAN of night, if I about shall go
For to deny my Master, do thou crow.
Thou stop'st Saint Peter in the midst of sin;
Stay me, by crowing, ere I do begin.
Better it is, premonished, for to shun
A sin, than fall to weeping when 'tis done.

Upon Time

TIME was upon
The wing, to fly away;
      And I called on
Him but awhile to stay;
      But he'd be gone,
For aught that I could say.

He held out then
A writing, as he went;
      And asked me when
False man would be content
      To pay again
What God and nature lent.

An hourglass,
In which were sands but few,
      As he did pass
He showed, and told me too
      My end near was,
And so away he flew.

A Thanksgiving to God, for His House

⚓

LORD, Thou hast given me a cell
      Wherein to dwell;
And little house, whose humble roof
      Is weather-proof,
Under the spars of which I lie
      Both soft and dry;
Where Thou my chamber for to ward
      Hast set a guard
Of harmless thoughts, to watch and keep
      Me while I sleep.

Low is my porch, as is my fate,
          Both void of state;
And yet the threshold of my door
          Is worn by the poor,
Who thither come and freely get
          Good words or meat.
Like as my parlor, so my hall
          And kitchen's small;
A little buttery, and therein
          A little bin
Which keeps my little loaf of bread
          Unchipped, unflayed;
Some brittle sticks of thorn or briar
          Make me a fire,
Close by whose living coal I sit,
          And glow like it.
Lord, I confess too, when I dine
          The pulse is thine,
And all those other bits that be
          There placed by Thee:
The worts, the purslain, and the mess
          Of watercress,
Which of thy kindness Thou hast sent;
          And my content
Makes those and my beloved beet
          To be more sweet.
'Tis Thou that crownest my glittering hearth
          With guiltless mirth,

And givest me wassail bowls to drink,
                    Spiced to the brink.
Lord, 'tis thy plenty-dropping hand
                    That soils my land,
And givest me, for my bushel sown,
                    Twice ten for one;
Thou makest my teeming hen to lay
                    Her egg each day;
Besides my healthful ewes to bear
                    Me twins each year;
The while the conduits of my kine
                    Run cream (for wine).
All these and better Thou dost send
                    Me to this end:
That I should render, for my part,
                    A thankful heart;
Which, fired with incense, I resign
                    As wholly thine;
But the acceptance, that must be,
                    My Christ, by Thee.

Welcome What Comes

⁂

WHATEVER comes, let's be content withal:
Among God's blessings, there is no one small.

Eternity

⁂

O YEARS and age! farewell:
    Behold I go
    Where I do know
Infinity to dwell.

And these my eyes shall see
    All times, how they
    Are lost in the sea
Of vast eternity.

Where never moon shall sway
    The stars, but she
    And night shall be
Drowned in one endless day.

To God, on His Sickness

♣

WHAT though my harp and viol be
Both hung upon the willow tree?
What though my bed be now my grave,
And for my house I darkness have?
What though my healthful days are fled,
And I lie numbered with the dead?
Yet I have hope, by Thy great power,
To spring, though now a withered flower.

Graces for Children

♣

WHAT GOD gives, and what we take,
'Tis a gift for Christ his sake:
Be the meal of beans and peas,
God be thanked for those and these:
Have we flesh, or have we fish,
All are fragments from his dish.
He his Church save, and the King,
And our peace here like a spring;
Make it ever flourishing.

Another Grace for a Child

⚜

HERE a little child I stand,
Heaving up my either hand;
Cold as paddocks* though they be,
Here I lift them up to Thee,
For a benison to fall
On our meat and on us all. Amen.

*Frogs or toads.

To His Dear God

❧

I'LL hope no more
For things that will not come;
And, if they do, they prove but cumbersome;
    Wealth brings much woe
    And, since it fortunes so,
    'Tis better to be poor,
        Than so to abound
        As to be drowned,
    Or overwhelmed with store.

    Pale care, avaunt,
    I'll learn to be content
With that small stock Thy bounty gave or lent.
    What may conduce
    To my most healthful use,
    Almighty God me grant;
        But that or this
        That hurtful is,
    Deny Thy suppliant.

To God

PARDON ME, God (once more I Thee entreat)
That I have placed Thee in so mean a seat,
Where round about Thou seest but all things vain,
Uncircumcised, unseasoned, and profane.
But as Heaven's public and immortal eye
Looks on the filth, but is not soiled thereby,
So Thou, my God, mayest on this impure look,
But take no tincture from my sinful book:
Let but one beam of glory on it shine,
And that will make me and my work divine.

His Wish to God

I WOULD to God that my old age might have
Before my last but here a living grave,
Some one poor almshouse: there to lie or stir
Ghostlike, as in my meaner sepulcher;
A little piggin and a pipkin by
To hold things fitting my necessity;
Which rightly used both in their time and place
Might me excite to fore- and after-grace.
Thy cross, my Christ, fixed 'fore my eyes should be,
Not to adore that, but to worship Thee.
So, here the remnant of my days I'd spend,
Reading Thy Bible and my book; so end.

The White Island

In this world (the Isle of Dreams)
While we sit by sorrow's streams,
Tears and terrors are our themes
     Reciting:

But when once from hence we fly,
More and more approaching nigh
Unto young eternity
     Uniting:

In that whiter Island, where
Things are evermore sincere;
Candor here, and lustre there
     Delighting:

There no monstrous fancies shall
Out of hell an horror call,
To create (or cause at all)
     Affrighting.

There in calm and cooling sleep
We our eyes shall never steep;
But eternal watch shall keep,
            Attending

Pleasures, such as shall pursue
Me immortalized, and you;
And fresh joys, as never too
            Have ending.

Martha, Martha

*

THE repetition of the name made known
No other than Christ's full affection.

His Meditation upon Death

BE THOSE few hours which I have yet to spend
Blessed with the meditation of my end:
Though they be few in number, I'm content;
If otherwise, I stand indifferent:
Nor makes it matter, Nestor's years to tell,
If man lives long and if he live not well.
A multitude of days still heaped on
Seldom brings order, but confusion.
Might I make choice, long life should be withstood,
Nor would I care how short it were if good;
Which to effect, let every passing bell
Possess my thoughts, next comes my doleful knell:
And when the night persuades me to my bed
I'll think I'm going to be burièd:
So shall the blankets which come over me
Present those turfs which once must cover me:
And with as firm behavior I will meet
The sheet I sleep in, as my windingsheet.
When sleep shall bathe his body in my eyes
I will believe that then my body dies:
And if I chance to wake and rise thereon,
I'll have in mind my resurrection,
Which must produce me to that general doom
To which the peasant, so the prince, must come,

To hear the Judge give sentence on the throne,
Without the least hope of affection.
Tears at that day shall make but weak defense,
When hell and horror fright the conscience.
Let me, though late, yet at the last begin
To shun the least temptation to a sin;
Though to be tempted be no sin, until
Man to the alluring object gives his will.
Such let my life assure me, when my breath
Goes thieving from me, I am safe in death;
Which is the height of comfort: when I fall,
I rise triumphant in my funeral.

No Coming to God without Christ

*

GOOD and great God! How should I fear
To come to Thee, if Christ not there!
Could I but think He would not be
Present, to plead my cause for me;
To hell I'd rather run, than I
Would see thy face and He not by.

To God

*

THE WORK is done; now let my laurel be
Given by none but by thyself to me:
That done, with honor Thou dost me create
Thy poet and thy prophet laureate.

INDEX OF TITLES

INDEX OF FIRST LINES

Her eyes the glowworm lend thee, *16*
Here a little child I stand, *112*
Here, here I live with what my board, *73*
Here she lies in bed of spice, *91*

I bring ye love: *Quest. What will love do?*, *93*
I dare not ask a kiss, *83*
I do not love to wed, *64*
I have been wanton and too bold, I fear, *96*
I make no haste to have my Numbers read, *80*
I saw a fly within a bead, *90*
I sing of brooks, of blossoms, birds, and bowers, *15*
I would to God that my old age might have, *115*
If ye fear to be affrighted, *94*
If you will with Mab find grace, *74*
I'll hope no more, *113*
I'll write, because I'll give, *21*
In the hour of my distress, *103*
In the morning when ye rise, *94*
In this little urn is laid, *89*
In this world (the Isle of Dreams), *116*

Julia, I bring, *30*

Let us (though late) at last (my Silvia) wed, *78*
Loath to depart, but yet at last each one, *59*
Look how our foul days do exceed our fair, *101*
Lord, Thou hast given me a cell, *107*

Man may want land to live in; but for all, *89*
More discontents I never had, *19*
My faithful friend, if you can see, *41*
My God! look on me with thine eye, *102*

Noonday and midnight shall at once be seen, *29*
Not all thy flushing suns are set, *36*
Now is the time for mirth, *42*

O! times most bad, *75*
O years and age! farewell, *110*
One night in the year, my dearest beauties, come, *81*
Only a little more, *46*

Pardon me, God (once more I Thee entreat), *114*
Praise they that will times past, I joy to see, *93*